YOU CAN TELL ME ANYTHING

By Elizabeth A. Peck

Illustrated by Loïs Cordelia

Caritate

You Can Tell Me Anything by Elizabeth A. Peck
Illustrated by Loïs Cordelia
First edition 2023

Published by Caritate, an imprint of The Franciscan Publishing Company Ltd,
Darlington, Co. Durham, England.

ISBN 9781915198204

Cover design and typesetting by Steve Buchanan

All profits from the sale of this book will be donated to EducAid Sierra Leone.
Charity no. 1163161.

Printed by Newton Press, Blue Bridge Centre, St Cuthbert's Way, Newton Aycliffe DL5 6DS
on sustainably sourced paper and card, using vegetable based inks on a waterless printing press.

FSC

For all members of the EducAid community.

You can tell me anything.
There's nothing you could say
That could ever, ever make me
Love you less, or go away.

You know that you can tell me all
About your day at school -
Your lessons, what you had for lunch,
Who bent or broke a rule,

But you can tell me other things,
Like what you're scared of too.
I'll always listen, never laugh;
I promise you, it's true!

You can tell me if you're frightened
When we dim the light at night.
You can tell me if you're worried,
If there's something just 'not right'.

Or if there's ever someone
With whom you're not at ease
You can absolutely tell me;
I will never, ever tease.

You can tell me if you're anxious when
We have to be apart.
You can tell me any fear or worry
Churning in your heart.

If you make a bad decision,
If you haven't been your best,
If you get that sorry feeling,
That sinking in your chest,

A tightening in your tummy,
If you feel a bit ashamed,
I will listen without anger;
I will love you just the same.

Perhaps you lost your temper
And broke a toy in rage;
Perhaps you acted selfishly,
Or scribbled on a page;

Perhaps you really hurt someone
With words or looks or hands;
Perhaps you know you've wounded
Someone's heart - I'll understand.

I couldn't bear to think of you
Upset or sad alone.
Please trust me; let me carry it,
And make your pain my own.

Don't worry it could hurt me.
It might - but that's ok!
I'm strong enough to take it;
Throw your sadness all my way!

There's nothing bad or naughty
That you can't admit to me,
As I'll forgive you anything,
Whatever it might be.

But listen! You can also share
Your dreams of every kind,
The wishes and imaginings
That sparkle in your mind.

What is it that you wish were real,
Or dream that you could do?
Breathe underwater, fly in space?
I'd love it if I knew!

And what is it you hope for,
Things more possible, I mean?
From clothes or shoes to sweets and treats -
A special toy you've seen?

It could be that you want a friend
Who sees things just like you,
Who likes your games and shares your aims,
Who's kind and good and true.

There's nothing you could wish for
That I wouldn't want to hear.
You can write it down or shout it out,
Or whisper in my ear.

Tell me, too, what brings you joy,
What makes your soul delight!
I promise that I'll cherish what you say
With all my might.

You can tell me if you want to simply
Gawp and gaze and stare
At the moon, the stars, a sunset,
At the beauty everywhere.

And as you grow much bigger,
This will all remain the same.
Your fears and worries, plans and hopes,
Mistakes, bad choices, pain,

Your big ambitions, tough dilemmas,
Wishes, prayers, or will:
There's nothing you can't say to me;
I'll be here, listening still.

Yes -

You can tell me anything.
There's nothing you could say
That could ever, ever make me
Love you less, or go away.

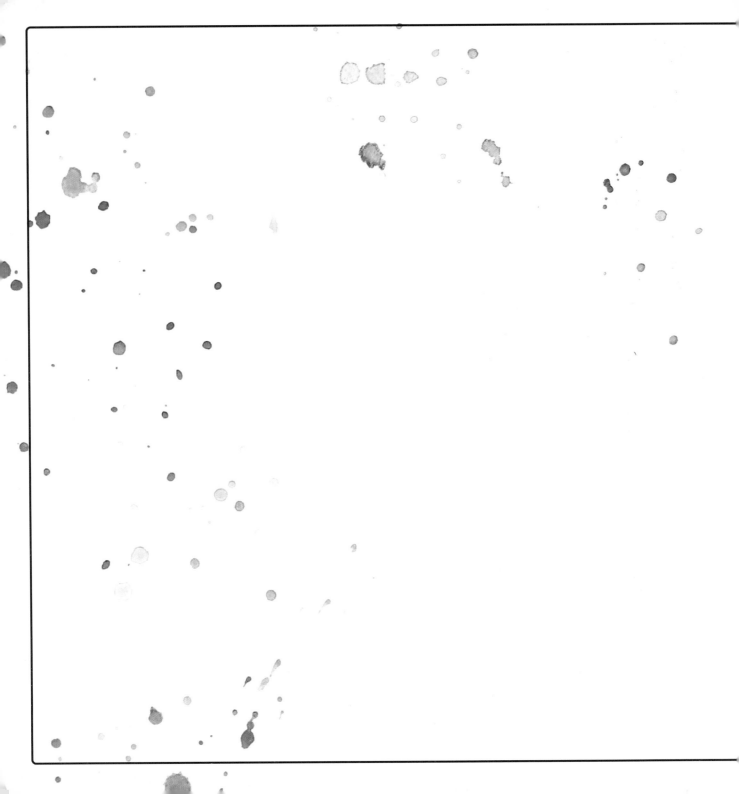